Hey! Take a look at the profiles of these five, noble Vikings. Can you tell by looking which one is loyal and obedient to a fault? Which one has a craving for imported goods? Which one's hair length is a disgrace to the rest of the family? Which one wouldn't be caught dead without metal armor? And, which one is the fiercest barbarian ever to set sail?

You can't tell? Well, you're about to join the more than 35 million readers of Dik Browne's comic strip who could tell *you* a thing or two.

Meet Hagar the Horrible; the wife, Helga; their two lovely children, Hamlet and Honi; and Lucky Eddie, Hagar's sidekick. They'll plunder your heart and do havoc with your funny bone.

HÄGAR

THE HORRIBLE
ON THE RACK #5

BY DIK BROWNE

**tempo
books**

GROSSET & DUNLAP
A FILMWAYS COMPANY
Publishers • New York

OH, THESE STAINS WON'T COME OUT!

YOU'VE GOT BLOOD-STAINS ALL OVER YOUR GOOD SHIRT!

DIK BROWNE 2-18

WELL, DON'T BLAME ME — THEY'RE NOT MINE!

3-5
DIK BROWNE-

DIK BROWNE — 3-16

HELGA SAYS WE GOTTA HAVE THE CORRECT WINE TO GO WITH OUR DINNER

WHAT ARE YOU HAVING FOR DINNER?

DIK BROWNE

4-1

LEFTOVERS

LISTEN! NOBODY EVER HANDED ME ANYTHING ON A SILVER PLATTER

HERE'S YOUR BEER, HAGAR

WILL YOU BEAT IT! I'M TRYING TO MAKE A POINT!!

4-16

4-23

DIK BROWNE - 5-8

YOU'RE SPOILING HIM—
HE NEEDS DISCIPLINE

YOU DON'T
WANT HIM
TO GROW
UP WILD

5-15

HE GETS HAIR
ALL OVER THE
FURNITURE

DIK
BROWNE

THEY MUST BE
TALKING ABOUT
YOU, SNERT

WHY DO VIKINGS WEAR HORNS, DAD?

I'LL TELL YOU IF YOU PROMISE NOT TO TELL YOUR MOTHER ---

DIK BROWNE 9-5

THEY'RE REALLY EAR PLUGS.